SPOTLIGHT ON...

Figurative Language

W9-BRX-570

NEW YORK · TORONTO · LONDON · AUCKLAND · SYDNEY
MEXICO CITY · NEW DELHI · HONG KONG · BUENOS AIRES

Teaching *Resources*

Acknowledgments

"Boar Out There" by Cynthia Rylant. Reprinted with the permission of Atheneum Books for Young Readers, an imprint of Simon & Schuster Children's Publishing Division from EVERY LIVING THING by Cynthia Rylant. Copyright © 1985 by Cynthia Rylant.

"Sir Gawain and the Green Knight" by Pat Cusick. Copyright © 2004 by Pat Cusick. All rights reserved.

"The Jewels of the Sea" from THE DANCING KETTLE AND OTHER JAPANESE FOLK TALES by Yoshiko Uchida. Copyright © 1986 by Yoshiko Uchida. Published by Creative Arts Book Company.

Excerpt from OUT OF THE DUST by Karen Hesse. Copyright © 1997 by Karen Hesse. Published by Scholastic Inc. Reprinted by permission of Scholastic Inc.

"Seven Ways of Looking at the Moon" by Xenia Protopopescu from METAPHORS & SIMILES YOU CAN EAT by Orel Protopopescu. Copyright © 2003 by Orel Protopopescu. Published by Scholastic Inc. All rights reserved.

"A Thundery Day" by Susan Meader from MIRACLES: POEMS BY CHILDREN OF THE ENGLISH-SPEAKING WORLD edited by Richard Lewis. Simon and Schuster, 1966. Copyright © 1966 by Richard Lewis. Used with the permission of Richard Lewis, Touchstone Center for Children, Inc.

ISBN 0-439-65983-3

Contents

Sir Gawain and the Green Knight

A retelling of a King Arthur legend

BY PAT CUSICK

Winter held Britain in an icy grip. Snow covered the forest and field, and a lone wolf howled at the cold moon. Mists rose and fell over the marshland, and under the earth, the great trolls moaned in their sleep. But high on the hill, lights and music filled the shimmering castle. King Arthur was observing the New Year at Camelot. His knights and their ladies were celebrating with him.

Arthur was the noblest knight of all, a man of great wisdom and courage. He had carefully selected the Knights of the Round Table. They were the finest warriors in all of Britain and they fought nobly at his side. Each had sworn to abide by the Code of Chivalry. The Code required that they fight for king and country, support and defend the rights of the weak.

Tonight Arthur sat with the beautiful Queen Guenevere on a high dais. Beside the royal couple sat his young nephew, Sir Gawain. Arthur's heart was filled with joy as he greeted one person and then another. When everyone was seated, the trumpets sounded, and the first course arrived. Servants carried in huge platters of venison and great bowls of soup and placed them before the guests. Arthur laughed and talked as his guests ate and drank.

Everyone was enjoying the food and the fellowship, when a loud crash sounded at the gate. The huge doors swung open, and a gigantic knight on an immense horse rode into the hall. He was dressed in bright green from top to toe. His heavy green coat was lined with green leather. His stockings were green and the toes on his shoes were tipped with green and gold. Around his waist he wore a wide green belt set with sparkling emeralds. Smaller emeralds decorated the saddle of his handsome horse, which was the same bright green color as his coat. The knight's hair was rich and full and gleamed green in the candlelight. Those in the hall were speechless as they gazed at the sight.

The Green Knight wore no armor and carried no sword. In his right hand he held a branch of holly, and in his left he carried a huge ax. It was large and heavy to hold, and its blade had been sharpened to cut as close as a razor. The Green Knight rode boldly into the room, looking neither to the left or right, until he reached the front of the hall. He reined in his horse and stared at the knights before him.

"Which one is your leader?" he thundered. "I would speak to him courteously, as the Code of Chivalry requires."

Arthur broke the silence.

"Fair knight, welcome to this place. I am Arthur, the chief of this company. We would be happy to have you partake of our feast."

Then the Green Knight looked straight at Arthur and replied, "You and your knights are known far and wide as the best and bravest knights in the world. I come to you in peace, for I carry a branch of holly in my hand. But I would challenge your knights to a game in honor of the New Year, the time of gift-giving."

The Green Knight stood high in his stirrups and waited. No one moved. He shook his fist at the knights and then began to laugh, saying, "Is this the glorious Round Table? Will no one pick up my challenge? Are you, the bravest knights in the world, afraid to answer me?"

Arthur stood up and shouted, "No man in this great hall fears you. I will take your challenge and meet your terms. With this very ax I will break every bone in your body!" And Arthur grasped the ax from the knight's hands, waving it to the right and the left, testing its strength.

The Knights of the Round Table watched, as still as stones. Then young Gawain leaped to his feet and ran to the king.

"Oh, noble king!" he pleaded, "Let me take this challenge. It is not right that you, our leader, should respond to this knight's words. This is a foolish contest, but it is suitable for me, the least brave and least worthy of all your knights. If I fail, then let the blame be mine and in no way let it be placed with you or this noble company."

Arthur listened, a smile coming over his face. He moved from table to table, consulting with his knights. All agreed that Gawain should take this challenge.

So the king offered the green ax to Sir Gawain with these words, "Be strong, nephew, and strike carefully. If you do, I believe you will be able to survive his stroke when it is your turn, a year and a day from today."

Then Arthur stepped back. Everyone watched as Gawain, ax in hand, approached the Green Knight.

"I am Gawain," he said to the Green Knight. "Let it be known that Gawain gives you this blow. A year and a day from now, you may deliver the same kind of blow to me. No matter what weapon you choose, I will be ready."

The Green Knight's laughter filled the hall and he leaned toward the young knight saying, "Hail to you, Gawain. I am pleased to receive this blow from your hand. And I accept your pledge to return the favor. But you must seek me out and find me, wherever I may be, and you must come alone."

"I do not know your home, so how shall I find you?" asked Gawain. "Tell me your kingdom and your name and I will most certainly appear as I promised."

"Not yet," said the Green Knight. "First, deliver the blow. If you strike squarely, then I will tell you how to find me so you can fulfill the bargain. Take up your weapon, Sir, and let us see whether or not you can deliver a proper blow."

With that, the Green Knight knelt down on the floor. He bent his head and pushed his long, thick hair to one side so that his neck was clearly in view. Gawain stood above him, ax in hand. He placed one foot in front of the other. Then he grasped the ax tightly and lifted it high in the air, bringing it down in one swift stroke. It pierced the Green Knight's bare neck and sliced through his flesh and bones.

The Green Knight's head flew into the air and came crashing to the ground. As it rolled across the floor, some of the knights kicked it to one another, beginning a grisly game of sport. Although blood poured from the Green Knight's body, covering his green clothing with brilliant red, he wasted not a second. Headless, he leaped to his feet and jumped into the crowd of playful knights, snatching his head up by the hair. Then he ran to his horse and hoisted himself into the saddle. He held his head high in the air for all to see.

The knights were filled with horror as the headless body turned this way and that, the blood still streaming to the ground. Then the Green Knight turned his bleeding head toward the crowd, and the eyelids opened. The face looked directly upon Gawain, the

mouth moved, and the lips began to speak.

"Do not forget, Gawain, the promise you made in this hall tonight. Let a year and a day go by, and then seek me faithfully. I am known as the Knight of the Green Chapel. You must come to me and offer your neck as I did to receive a blow. You will find me if you try. If you do not, you will be called a coward by the world for the rest of your days!"

Without another word, the knight pulled his horse around and galloped away. King Arthur turned to Guenevere and said, "It is a season of magic, my dear queen, and we have all just seen a marvel unlike anything we have ever seen before. Rest your heart, and do not fear. Magic and wondrous events often take place during the New Year. So enjoy the music of the minstrels and the laughter and conversation of our knights and ladies!"

Then Arthur smiled at Gawain and said, "Hang your ax on the wall above our table. Let us all admire it and wonder at this strange adventure that took place tonight."

The feast ended and the New Year began. Spring came, followed by summer, followed by autumn. Gawain had many adventures, but when winter arrived, he set out to seek the Knight of the Green

Chapel and keep his pledge.

One day Gawain found himself before a strange castle. He approached the guard and was brought inside. He explained to the lord of the castle that he was searching for the Knight of the Green Chapel. The lord invited him to stay and rest a few days before continuing his search.

Then the lord suggested that they play a game.

"Each day I will go out to hunt, and each day you will stay here and rest. At the end of the day, I will offer you whatever I have won in the forest. You will offer me whatever you have won in my home," he said.

Gawain agreed, and the next day the lord went off to the hunt. During the day, the lady of the house spoke soft words to Gawain and walked with him about the castle grounds. At the end of the day, the lady offered Gawain a kiss. Gawain thought the lady was very beautiful. He wished to kiss her in return, but he pulled away, for she was the wife of his host.

That evening the lord of the castle offered Gawain a deer, and Gawain offered him a kiss.

The next day the game continued. This time the lord offered Gawain a boar, and the knight offered him two kisses.

On the third day, the lady kissed Gawain three

times. Then she offered him a green silk scarf to wear beneath his armor.

"Green is a magic color," she said, "and this scarf is magical. Wear it when you bow your head before the Green Knight. The scarf will protect you."

That evening the lord offered Gawain a fox, and Gawain gave him three kisses. But he said nothing about the green scarf. The next morning, after thanking the lord for his hospitality, he rode out of the castle to seek the Green Knight.

He passed a bubbling brook and heard someone sharpening an ax. Gawain followed the sound. The man who was sharpening the ax was the Green Knight. Although his heart was filled with fear, Gawain spoke boldly to him.

"I am Gawain, here to fulfill my pledge," he said. "Never let it be said that Gawain did not keep a promise."

"And I am here to fulfill the terms of the agreement," said the Green Knight as he picked up his ax.

His heart pounding, Gawain knelt and offered his neck to the Green Knight. The knight lifted his ax high to deliver the fatal blow. As the blade descended, Gawain could hear the sharp blade slicing through the air—and he flinched!

The Green Knight stopped and set his ax aside, scolding the young knight for his cowardice. But Gawain leaped to his feet and begged for another chance. The Green Knight agreed to try again. This time, as the blade descended and sliced through the air, Gawain did not flinch, but the Knight stopped the blade. He asked the young knight to face him and bare his throat. With the edge of his blade, the Green Knight nicked Gawain's throat.

Gawain leaped to his feet saying, "Now the pledge is fulfilled, Knight of the Green Chapel. I challenge you to a battle of sword against ax!"

The Green Knight threw back his head and began to laugh, his voice ringing through the forest. "Why, Gawain, are you so angry?" he said. "Why should you challenge me? Did I treat you discourteously? Behold! You promised to allow me a blow. I attempted two blows, and I finally took a blow the third time. I could have injured you much more seriously, but I did not. I recalled how honestly you dealt me a blow on the evening I appeared in King Arthur's court."

The Green Knight continued. "The first blow simply frightened you. It was in honor of the first day that you spent in my castle. You gave me honestly what you had received, a single kiss from my wife. The

second blow was for the second day when you offered
me two kisses from my wife. For it is true, an honorable man need not fear danger."

Now the Green Knight looked at Gawain with a
steady eye. Gawain was as still as stone. The Green
Knight spoke again.

"But on the third day you did not behave as a true
and honest knight, and that is why there is a nick on
your throat. For on the third day, you took a sash that
belongs to me. You are wearing it now, a green silken
sash given to you by my wife. Ah yes, I know all about
my wife's kisses and how you restrained yourself. I set
it all up as a test for you. Truly, I believe you are one
of the most faultless knights that ever graced our
island. But you failed, however slightly. And you did
not do so out of an evil heart. You failed out of fear for
your own life. You loved your life more than honor,
and I cannot blame you for that."

Once again there was silence. Anguish filled the
heart of Gawain. He looked at the ground, then at the
heavens, and finally at the Green Knight.

"I have been untruthful and broken the Code of
Chivalry," he cried out. "I have brought shame upon
my name, Gawain of the Round Table. Because I
loved my life and feared your blow, I was false to you. I

regret it and wish to regain your good will."

The Green Knight laughed and said, "Gawain, be at peace. You have admitted wrongdoing and have taken the punishment from my ax. I hold you in good faith. I grant you the green scarf, as green as my robes, as a parting gift to begin the New Year."

As Gawain slipped on his helmet, he looked sadly at the Green Knight and said, "I leave you in great sorrow, and I thank you for your forgiveness. I accept your scarf, not for its beauty or for its magical properties, but as a sign of my failure. I will wear it on my arm always. When I accomplish great things and wish to lift my head above my fellow knights, this scarf will remind me of this day."

Then Gawain looked up at the Green Knight and asked, "Before I go, may I ask you your name?"

"I am happy to tell you," the Green Knight replied, "I am called Bercilak de Hautdesert. The beautiful goddess Morgan le Fay, mistress of Merlin, lives in my house. It is she who sent me to King Arthur's court to test the pride of his knights. Morgan le Fay is an excellent wizard. She intended to frighten you out of your wits by enabling me to speak even though my head had been cut from my body."

Gawain sighed. It was time for him to leave. He

embraced the Green Knight and pledged eternal friendship. As he began his journey to King Arthur's court, he thought about what had happened. He had been given his life back, a fine gift indeed. And he had learned how weak he could be.

Gawain had many adventures as he traveled the highways and byways of the kingdom. The wound in his neck healed. He wore the green sash under his left arm, its knotted ends flying in the breeze. And so one day, he entered Camelot again.

King Arthur was amazed, for he had feared Gawain would lose his life fulfilling his pledge. He embraced his nephew over and over. The knights insisted on celebrating with a great feast. Everyone wanted to hear his story.

Gawain told them all that had happened, sharing with them his untruthfulness and the goodwill of the Green Knight. He showed everyone the scar on his neck. Then he held up the green scarf and said to Arthur, "Behold the sign of my disgrace, which I wear like the scar on my neck. I will wear it all of my life to remind me that I once broke the Code of Chivalry and was untruthful to another knight. To my endless disgrace, I did it out of fear of losing my life."

Arthur embraced Gawain and tried to comfort him.

The rest of the knights told him how happy they were to see him again. They urged him to be at peace, for he had been honorable in all ways, except one. They promised, one and all, to wear a ribbon of bright green on their left arms in fellowship with him. From thenceforward, the Knights of the Round Table all wore a green ribbon to honor their beloved Gawain and his contest with the Green Knight.

Boar Out There

BY CYNTHIA RYLANT

Everyone in Glen Morgan knew there was a wild boar in the woods over by the Miller farm. The boar was out beyond the splintery rail fence and past the old black Dodge that somehow had ended up in the woods and was missing most of its parts.

Jenny would hook her chin over the top rail of the fence, twirl a long green blade of grass in her teeth and whisper, "Boar out there."

And there were times she heard him. She imagined him moving heavily through the trees, ignoring the sharp thorns and briars that raked his back and going away trembling.

She thought he might have a golden horn on his terrible head. The boar would run deep into the woods, then rise up on his rear hooves, throw his head back toward the stars and cry a long, clear, sure note, and the note would glide through the night toward the heart of the moon, Jenny knew, as she lay in bed, listening.

One hot summer day she went to find the boar. No one in Glen Morgan had ever gone past the old black Dodge and beyond, as far as she knew. But the boar was there somewhere between those awful trees, and his dark green eyes waited for someone.

Jenny felt it was she.

Moving slowly over damp brown leaves, Jenny could sense her ears tingle and fan out as she listened for thick breathing from the trees. She stopped to pick a teaberry leaf to chew, stood a minute, then went on.

Deep in the woods she kept her eyes to the sky. She needed to be reminded that there was a world above and apart from the trees—a world of space and air, air that didn't linger all about her, didn't press deep into her skin, as forest air did.

Finally, leaning against a tree to rest, she heard him for the first time. She forgot to breathe, standing there listening to the stamping of hooves, and she choked and coughed.

Coughed!

And now the pounding was horrible, too loud and confusing for Jenny. Horrible. She stood stiff with wet eyes and knew she could always pray, but for some reason didn't.

He came through the trees so fast that she had no time to scream or run. And he was there before her.

His large gray-black body shivered as he waited just beyond the shadow of the tree she held for support. His nostrils glistened, and his eyes; but astonishingly, he was silent. He shivered and glistened and was absolutely silent.

Jenny matched his silence, and her body was rigid, but not her eyes. They traveled along his scarred, bristling back to his thick hind legs. Tears spilling and flooding her face, Jenny stared at the boar's ragged ears, caked with blood. Her tears dropped to the leaves, and the only sound between them was his slow breathing

Then the boar snorted and jerked. But Jenny did not move.

High in the trees a bluejay yelled, and suddenly, it was over. Jenny stood like a rock as the boar wildly flung his head and in terror bolted past her.

Past her . . . .

And now, since that summer, Jenny still hooks her chin over the old rail fence, and she still whispers, "Boar out there." But when she leans on the fence, looking into the trees, her eyes are full and she leaves wet patches on the splintery wood. She is sorry for the torn ears of the boar and sorry that he has no golden horn.

But mostly she is sorry that he lives in fear of bluejays and little girls, when everyone in Glen Morgan lives in fear of him.

The Jewels of the Sea

A retelling of a Japanese folk tale

BY YOSHIKO UCHIDA

Once long, long ago in the land of Japan, there lived two young princes. The older prince was an excellent fisherman whose skill no one could ever equal. It was said that he could catch anything that swam in the sea. Now the younger prince was as skilled on land as his brother was at sea. He was the finest hunter in all the land,

and feared no animal that stalked through the woods and over the mountains of Japan. Each day the two set out together; the older brother would go toward the sea with his rod and reel, while the younger brother with his bow and a quiver full of arrows set forth for the mountains.

Now one morning as the two princes prepared to go out for the day, the younger brother said, "Each day for many years we have done the very same thing. You go to the sea and I to the mountains. I have grown weary of the same sport each day. Wouldn't you like to go hunting in my place today, while I go fishing in yours?"

"A good idea," said his brother. "I will take your bow and arrow and you shall take my rod and reel. Take care how you use them, however, for they are my most prized possessions."

So the older prince headed for the mountains and the younger prince for the sea. When the young prince reached the edge of the sea, he sat down among some boulders. He baited his hook with clumsy fingers, threw it into the water, and anxiously waited for the fish to bite. Each time the line moved just a little, he pulled it up to see what he had caught, but each time the hook came up empty.

Finally the sun began to sink slowly below the rim of the mountains, but still he had not caught a single fish. What's more, he had even lost his brother's very best hook.

"I must find my brother's hook," thought the young prince sadly, and he searched among the crevices of the boulders, and on the sands of the beach. As he was looking for the lost hook, his brother came back from the mountains. He too was empty-handed, for although he was an excellent fisherman, he could not hunt game.

"What are you looking for?" he called crossly to his younger brother.

"I have lost your precious hook," said the young prince, "and I have searched everywhere but cannot find it."

"Lost my hook?" shouted the older brother. "You see, this is what comes of your idea to change tasks for the day. If it hadn't been for your foolish idea, this never would have happened. You are a clumsy, blundering fool, and I shall not return your bow and arrow to you until you find my hook."

The young prince was very sad, and spent long hours searching for the lost hook. At last he began to think he would never find it by the sea, so he took his very best sword and broke it into hundreds of tiny pieces. Then he made five hundred beautiful hooks for his brother with the tiny pieces of his sword. He brought these to his brother saying, "Since I cannot find your lost hook, I have broken my sword and made five hundred new hooks for you. Please forgive me for having lost your precious hook."

But his older brother would not forgive him. The young prince made five hundred more hooks, but still his brother would not forgive him. He only said, "Even though you bring me a million hooks, I will not forgive you until you return the one hook you lost!"

So once again the young prince went to the seashore to see if the tide might have washed the lost hook up onto the sand. He roamed about sadly, walking back and forth along the beach where he had fished. Suddenly, from nowhere, there appeared an old man with hair as white as the clouds in the sky.

"Pray tell me, what is the young prince doing all alone, and why do you look so sad?" asked the old man.

So the young prince told him how he had lost his elder brother's hook, and how he could never be

forgiven until he found it again.

"But, my dear prince," said the old man kindly. "Surely your lost hook is at the bottom of the sea by this time, or at least in the belly of a fish. You will never find it here on the shore."

"Then what can I do?" asked the young prince.

"Why, the only thing you can do is to go to the King of the Sea and ask him to help you find it," answered the old man.

"That is an excellent idea!" said the prince. "But how will I ever get to his palace at the bottom of the sea?"

"Just leave everything to me," replied the old man. "I will help you get to his palace."

And so the old man made the prince a very special boat which could take him safely to the bottom of the sea. He then told him just how to get there, and wished him luck in finding his lost hook.

"Thank you, old man. You shall surely be rewarded when I return," said the young prince, and he sailed off for the palace of the King of the Sea.

He followed the old man's directions carefully, and before long he saw the sapphire roofs of the palace sparkling in the blue water. A large gate guarded the entrance, and the prince found it was locked tight.

"Oh, dear, how will I get in?" he thought as he looked around. Then he spied a lovely old tree growing by the gate. Its gnarled branches bent low and hung over a beautiful silver well.

"I shall just climb up on one of those branches and rest awhile," thought the prince. "Then someone may come along through the gates soon."

So he climbed up on one of the low branches and sat down to rest. Before long, the big gate of the palace slowly swung open. The prince looked down quickly and saw two beautiful maidens coming out of the gate carrying a lovely golden cup. They hurried toward the well and bent down to fill their cup with the clear, cool water. As they looked into the mirror-like water, they both cried out, for there, reflected in the stillness, was the face of the young prince.

They looked up at the tree in surprise, and saw the prince sitting quietly on one of the branches.

"I didn't mean to startle you," he said to the two maidens. "I have come a long way and just wanted to rest for a few minutes. I am very thirsty, and I see that you have a lovely golden cup. Will you give me a drink of water?"

"Why, of course," answered the two beautiful maidens.

When the prince had had his fill of water, he pulled a precious stone from a chain around his neck and dropped it into the golden cup before he returned it.

"Thank you for your kindness," he said. "I am looking for the King of the Sea. I wonder if you could help me find him?"

"Oh, but of course," answered the two lovely maidens, laughing gaily. "For we are his daughters!"

They hurried to tell their father of this strange visitor whom they had found sitting on the branch of the old tree by the well.

"Surely he is no ordinary mortal, for look at this beautiful stone which he dropped into our cup. It seems to be a *maga-tama*, a stone which is worn only by royalty."

The King of the Sea then called the young prince into his most beautiful room. "Now tell me what I can do for you," he said to the prince.

So the young prince told him who he was, and why he had come. He told him how he had lost his brother's hook and had come down to the bottom of the sea to seek help.

"Will you be good enough, kind sir, to search your kingdom for my brother's fishhook?" he asked.

"By all means, my good friend, by all means," replied the king, and he beckoned to one of his servants. "Call together all my subjects who live in the Kingdom of the Sea," he said.

The servant disappeared for a few moments and before long, all who lived in the great kingdom of the sea came swimming toward the palace of their king: giant tortoises and little clams; sea horses, crabs, and lobsters with long green claws; mackerels, sea bass, herrings, swordfish, and all the many, many fish in the sea. When they had all gathered in the great courtyard, the king stood before them and called out,

"We have a very important visitor with us today— a prince who has come down to the bottom of the sea to search for a lost fishing hook. If any among you have seen it, speak now and tell your king!"

The fish looked at each other and shook their shiny heads; the tortoise looked at the clam and slowly shook his head; the crabs and lobsters wriggled their feelers and looked about on the sand and in the coral. At last, from far back in the group a little silver fish came forward and spoke to the king.

"Oh, good King, I do believe it is my friend, the red snapper, who has swallowed the hook of our visiting prince."

"And why do you say that?" asked the king.

"Because, sir, he has been complaining of a sore throat and has eaten nothing for a long time. And you see, he is not present now, for I fear he is ill at home."

"Hmm, that *is* strange," said the king, "for the red snapper is usually the first to come to all our gatherings. Have him brought forth immediately."

Soon the red snapper was brought to the meeting. He looked pale and sickly, and his tail drooped on the sand.

"Yes, sir?" he answered in a low, weak voice. "Did you wish to see me?"

"Why did you not come when I called the fish of my kingdom?" asked the king.

"Because, sir, I have been very ill," moaned the red snapper. "I haven't been at all well for some time. My throat is sore, I cannot eat, and see—my fins will not stand up on my back. I fear something is very wrong indeed."

"He's swallowed the hook! He's swallowed the hook!" murmured all the fish of the sea.

"Then open his mouth and look," commanded the king. Two guards immediately opened wide the red

snapper's mouth, and peered down his throat. There they found the prince's shiny hook, and quickly removed it. The red snapper smiled happily, and so did the young prince. He thanked the guards and the king and all the subjects of the Kingdom of the Sea, for now at last he had recovered his brother's precious hook. Now at last his task was completed and he could return home once more. But the Kingdom of the Sea was so beautiful, and he was having such a pleasant time that he stayed on and on. Before he quite realized it, three long years had gone by. At last he went to the King of the Sea and said,

"I have spent three long and happy years here in your lovely Kingdom of the Sea, but I cannot stay forever. I must return to my own kingdom and to my own land above the waters."

The king turned to the young prince and said, "I hope that you of the land and we of the sea shall always be friends. As a token of our friendship, I wish you to take back with you two jewels of the sea." Then he called his servant, who came in with two large and beautiful jewels. They sparkled and glistened as the king held them in his hands.

The king raised the jewel in his right hand and said, "This stone has the power to call forth the waters of the sea. Raise it above your head and great waves will come rushing up about you no matter where you may be."

Then the king held up the jewel in his other hand. "Raise this stone above your head and no matter how high the seas that surround you may be, the waters will recede and be drawn away." Then he gave the two jewels to the prince.

"They are beautiful jewels, sir," said the prince. "And what wonderful powers they possess!"

"Keep them with you always," said the king, "and they will protect you from all danger and harm."

The prince thanked the good king and prepared to be on his way. He said farewell to his many friends in the Kingdom of the Sea, and then the king called a large alligator who was to carry the prince back again to land. This was an even stranger vessel than the one which had brought him to the bottom of the sea, but the alligator swam swiftly and smoothly, and soon the prince was standing safely on the very beach from which he had departed.

He hurried to his palace and holding the hook which he had found, he called to his older brother, "Here I am, back once again, and here is your precious hook at last!"

Now the older brother had seized the throne while the younger prince was away, thinking that his younger brother would never return. He was very happy that he alone was the great and powerful ruler of the land, so when the young prince appeared with the lost hook, he was not at all glad to see him. Dark and evil thoughts cropped up in his jealous mind, and soon he decided that he would kill his younger brother so that he could continue to be the only ruler of the land.

One day as the young prince was strolling about in the fields outside the palace, the older brother crept up behind him with a long dagger. He raised it high in the air and was about to stab the young prince. But the young prince turned quickly and remembered what the King of the Sea had told him. He reached for the jewels of the sea and raised one high over his head. At once great high waves came thundering over the fields. They crashed and roared about the older prince and swept him off his feet.

"Help, help, I'm drowning! Save me, save me!" he cried.

The young prince then reached for the other jewel and held it high over his head. The waters immediately began to recede and the waves rolled gently back again toward the sea. The older brother sat on the ground gasping for breath.

"Thank you for saving my life," he said to the young prince. "You must have a power far greater than I, to be able to command the waters of the sea to come and go when you choose. I have done you a great injustice and I hope you will forgive me."

The kind young prince was quick to forgive his older brother and before long they were once again the best of friends. From that day on, they ruled together over a land of peace and plenty.

Excerpt from

Out of the Dust

BY KAREN HESSE

Fields of Flashing Light

I heard the wind rise,
and stumbled from my bed,
down the stairs,
out the front door,
into the yard.
The night sky kept flashing,
lightning danced down on its spindly legs.
I sensed it before I knew it was coming.
I heard it,
smelled it,
tasted it.
Dust.

While Ma and Daddy slept,
the dust came,
tearing up fields where the winter wheat,
set for harvest in June,
stood helpless.
I watched the plants,
surviving after so much drought and so much wind,
I watched them fry,
or flatten,
or blow away,
like bits of cast-off rags.

It wasn't until the dust turned toward the house,
like a fired locomotive,
and I fled,
barefoot and breathless, back inside,
it wasn't until the dust
hissed against the windows,
until it ratcheted the roof,
that Daddy woke.

He ran into the storm,
his overalls half-hooked over his union suit.
"Daddy!" I called. "You can't stop dust."

Ma told me to
cover the beds,
push the scatter rugs against the doors,
dampen the rags around the windows.
Wiping dust out of everything,
she made coffee and biscuits,
waiting for Daddy to come in.

Sometime after four,
rubbing low on her back,
Ma sank down into a chair at the kitchen table
and covered her face.
Daddy didn't come back for hours,
not
until the temperature dropped so low,
it brought snow.

Ma and I sighed, grateful,
staring out at the dirty flakes,
but our relief didn't last.
The wind snatched that snow right off the fields,
leaving behind a sea of dust,
waves and
waves and
waves of
dust, rippling across our yard.

Daddy came in,
he sat across from Ma and blew his nose.
Mud streamed out.
He coughed and spit out
mud.
If he had cried,
his tears would have been mud too,
but he didn't cry.
And neither did Ma.

March 1934

Seven Ways of Looking at the Moon

BY XENIA PROTOPOPESCU

1

The window in the night
Lets us glimpse the brightness
Of the coming day.

2

The round shiny seal
Holds the ends
Of the black envelope together.

3

When the orange flame
Is extinguished in the black water,
All that is left
Is a white round candle.

4

When you are lost in the blackness,
The moon sends down a soft arm
To comfort you and point out the way.

5

The light at the end of the pendulum
Arcs back and forth across the night,
Hypnotizing the world to sleep.

6

The day shrinks
Until all that is left
Is a bright spot
Surrounded by nothingness.

7

The eye of the night
 Surveys its sleeping children.

A Thundery Day

BY SUSAN MEADER

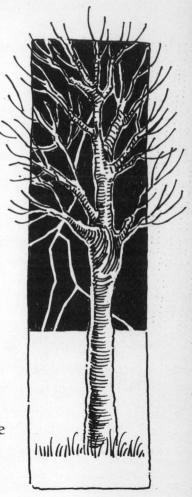

Soiled clouds hang;
A clap of thunder booms
Afar.
The air is hotly still;
Not a breath of wind and
We are restless.

A tree stands,
The monarch of the field,
Moving not a leaf.
Suddenly
The electricity of the sky
Flashes
And lets us glimpse
The counterpane of earth.
Clouds gather in a conference
And then the welcome rain
Comes pattering.